KEEP CALM!

Gifted to key-worker children by the author, a former Stebb teacher.

♡

(44) of 50

A STUDIO PRESS BOOK

First published in the UK in 2020 by Studio Press,
an imprint of Bonnier Books UK,
The Plaza, 535 King's Road, London SW10 0SZ

www.studiopressbooks.co.uk
www.bonnierbooks.co.uk

1 3 5 7 9 10 8 6 4 2

ISBN 978-1-78741-880-6

Written by Dr. Sharie Coombes
Illustrations by Katie Abey and Ellie O'Shea
Edited by Frankie Jones
Designed by Rob Ward

A CIP catalogue for this book is available from the British Library
Printed and bound in the United Kingdom

KEEP CALM!

AN ACTIVITY BOOK TO HELP YOUNG PEOPLE
CARRY ON DURING AND AFTER CORONAVIRUS

WELCOME TO KEEP CALM!

Author
DR. SHARIE COOMBES
Child and Family
Psychotherapist

CORONAVIRUS

That's a word you'd probably
never heard until recently, right?

And now it's all anyone seems to be
talking and thinking about, at home, on
the television and all over the internet.

Coronavirus is the reason schools closed down for
most young people. Everyone was told to stay at home
and life changed almost overnight all over the world.

No more going to the park, seeing friends or going to
events like parties, celebrations and sports meetings.

Many adults are working from home alongside
you as you're doing your schoolwork.

Some adults are still going to jobs outside of the
home if they are essential to keeping everything
running as well as helping people who need them.

We're living through unusual times and you'll probably hear many new words. It's likely you'll find yourself missing your friends and family. It wouldn't be surprising if all this sudden change makes you feel worried, confused and maybe even a bit scared or upset. At the same time, there might be things you're enjoying too.

This book will help you understand what is happening in the world and in yourself, find ways to express and accept your emotions and manage the feelings you experience until everything goes back to normal. We don't know when that will be yet, but things will go back to normal at some point quite soon.

For now, we can **KEEP CALM!** and carry on together with support from each other...

The activities in this book will show you how to feel more comfortable with the current uncertainty, stay safe, enjoy the positives, find hidden advantages, look forward to the future, and talk to others about your concerns and worries (if you want to).

You could use this book in a quiet, cosy place where you can think and feel relaxed. It's up to you which pages you do and when you do them, whether that's a page a day or lots of pages at once.

You can start anywhere in the book and you can even come back to a page many times. There are no rules. It's your book — do it your way!

You could show the activities to adults to explain how you're feeling and get any support you need.

There's also a section for adults at the back on how they can support you — make sure you show this to your parents, carers or guardians.

You can also contact these organisations who've helped thousands of children with every kind of worry and will know how to help you.

They won't be shocked by anything you tell them, however bad it seems to you.

YOUNG MINDS

Mental health and wellbeing information, advice and help for all children and young people.

Online information and advice as well as a free, confidential Crisis Messenger text-line available 24/7 across the UK.

Text: YM to 85258
www.youngminds.org.uk

CHILDLINE

Help and advice about a wide range of issues.

Comforts, advises and protects children and young people 24 hours a day and offers free, confidential counselling on helpline, online chat and Ask Sam.

Tel: 0800 1111
www.childline.org.uk

KEEP CALM!

This is an unusual time in history and we are all living through it together right around the world — YOU ARE NOT ALONE!

Our brains like life to be predictable, familiar and safe. When things change suddenly or seem strange to us, we can sometimes feel unsafe and even a bit scared or worried. This is because of Bob!

THIS IS BOB

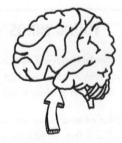

BOB'S PROPER NAME IS THE AMYGDALA

Bob is your brain's very own loving but sometimes daft guard dog who lives in an ancient part of your brain called the limbic system.

Bob wants to keep you safe at all times. If he spots anything unusual that could possibly become a problem, however tiny, he barks and blasts your body with brain chemicals.

These chemicals give you emotions that make you want to hide, fight or run away — we call this freeze, fight and flight.

All mammals have a Bob to protect them and most Bobs behave the same way.

Bob will take any tricky thoughts or emotions and turn them into feelings. He makes you feel all sorts of things, such as confused, shocked, frustrated, sad, angry, anxious, bored, lost or alone.

When you KEEP CALM!, you'll train Bob so that you can enjoy life and trust yourself to cope with the new situation.

And when you've learnt how to KEEP CALM!, you'll be able to do it long into the future even when everything is back to normal. Ready? Let's KEEP CALM!

Whenever Bob pops up on the page, you know the activity is a perfect treat for training Bob to KEEP CALM! Come back to this page whenever you need to remind yourself why Bob is barking at you.

HOW TO USE THIS BOOK

You could find yourself a notebook to do the activities in.

You could also use sheets of paper and staple, glue, sew or tie these together to make your own notebook or just keep them loose or in a folder. You could decorate a cereal box with wrapping paper to make a folder if you don't have one, or turn it inside out and draw on it.

Lots of the activities will suggest that you draw or write – you can choose to do them in whatever way you prefer. If you like to write, do that or if you like to draw, do that.

Or you can do both, if that's what you like!

ME, WHATEVER!

You are you, even during these unusual and difficult times.
Draw a picture of yourself and make your name zing on the page!

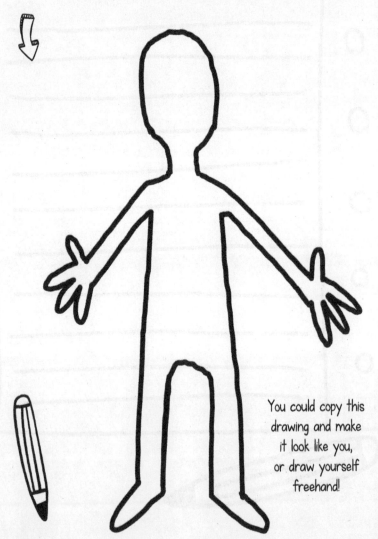

You could copy this
drawing and make
it look like you,
or draw yourself
freehand!

Write down or tell Bob 10 facts about you.

Include information about people, beliefs, things or causes you care about as well as facts about your appearance, age, where you live and who you live with.

During the coronavirus pandemic, you'll learn new things and have new experiences which may affect or change how you feel about the world and your life but you will still be YOU!

Here are some ideas to help you with your facts:

I am __ years old.

I live with _____.

My favourite hobby is _____.

My eyes are _____.

I like to eat _____.

My best friend is _____.

KEEP A TRY-ARY

In this book, you'll find lots of tips and techniques to try to help you KEEP CALM!

Why not keep a TRY-ARY to record which activities you've tried, when you tried them and how much they helped?

COPY THIS GRID INTO YOUR NOTEBOOK AND FILL IT IN. YOU CAN ADD EXTRA BOXES AS YOU NEED THEM!

TRIANGLE BREATHING, SATURDAY, 8/10			

Fill in the name of the activity and the dates you tried them.

You can also scale them from 0 to 10 depending on how much you enjoyed them or how helpful they were. 10 means it was great.

WHENEVER YOU NEED A KEEP CALM! BOOST, COME BACK TO THIS PAGE AND REMIND YOURSELF HOW.

NEW WORLD, NEW WORD

You'll probably have heard some new words since the pandemic started. Understanding new words helps Bob to KEEP CALM! Let's get him up to date so you can get on with having fun:

Virus: a type of infectious material that grows inside the cells of living things.

Coronavirus: a type of virus that looks like it has a crown around the outside under a microscope.

COVID-19: the illness caused by the newest coronavirus.

Self-isolation or shielding: when you stay at home to protect yourself and others from the virus.

Quarantine: when you stay in one room away from others if you have an illness that they could catch. You still have people coming in to look after you.

Lockdown: when everyone in the country stays at home. Key workers still go to work to take care of their community.

Social distancing: when you keep at least 2 metres away from people who don't live with you.

Epidemic: when a disease spreads across a community or country.

Pandemic: when a disease spreads across the world.

Antibodies: cells your blood makes to fight a disease during an infection to help you recover.

Vaccine: a substance that you're given to protect you from catching a disease.

Keep a list of any other new words you hear and ask or research what they mean.

Maybe you've noticed some new or unusual feelings recently. Use your imagination to create your own new words to describe them. You can ask your whole family to join in with this – why not get everyone thinking about it together? Start a video chat and see what you can all come up with...

HERE ARE SOME IDEAS:

distance-sadness   isoloneliness   clap-thankful

YES WE CAN!

At times, you might feel a bit overwhelmed during the pandemic. Remember, we have amazing scientists who can beat this and life will return to normal.

Look at the picture and notice the determined look on the character's face and in the body language.

Practise the YES WE CAN! pose by yourself in the mirror, as well as with your family, your pets and friends through video chatting.

You could ask someone to take a photograph of you doing it or draw yourself.

ICEBERGS AHEAD

We can usually only see a very small amount of
what people are feeling underneath the surface.

Think about your own deeper feelings for a moment. Draw an iceberg
and the water line. You can copy the one on this page, if you'd like.

Above the water, write what feelings you have or behaviour you
show that others might be able to see. Under the water, write or
draw what is going on for you that others might not be able to see.

Show this to adults if you need help with any of your feelings.

When you know what's under the surface, it's easier to KEEP CALM!

Other people have icebergs too. Draw another iceberg and
water line and write what feelings or actions you can
see in someone else, like a parent, sibling or pet.
Now fill in the underneath feelings they might be having.

Ask them how they are and let them know you care how they're feeling.
You could offer them a hug or suggest reading or playing a game
together, help them with a job or just listen to them.

You can do this activity whenever you want to try to
understand other people's feelings, or your own.

Why not make a poster of the iceberg for the fridge door and
make cards from old cereal boxes to write different feeling words on?
Using sticky-tac you can then add and take away some words
each day depending on how you're feeling. You could keep your
feeling word cards in a decorated jar or envelope.

SCARED

BORED

FED UP

CALM

TIRED

FIZZY

CHEERFUL

FRUSTRATED

TENSE

LONELY

CURIOUS

CONFUSED

PROUD

BUZZY

SATISFIED

MISSING

WORRIED

ENERGETIC

EXCITED

WORRY SIGNALS

Your body might feel strange if you are worrying about the coronavirus or home schooling or anything else.

This is true at all times, not just during the pandemic.

Here are some things you might notice and if you do, it means Bob is barking on the inside.

You'll need to do some of activities in this book to help you both KEEP CALM!

Check out your TRY-ARY to remind yourself which ones you love best or just flick through the book until you find something you want to do.

Hot or cold face

Dizzy, faint or
lightheaded

Hard to
swallow

Fast breathing

Tight chest

Racing or
fluttery heart

Sweaty palms

Numb or
tingly hands

Feeling sick

Hot or cold
waves

Feeling strange
or separate from
everyone else

Upset
tummy

Use this page to explain to an adult what
is happening and talk about it together.

DOODLE-ICIOUS

Start in the bottom corner of a piece of paper or notebook page and draw a line all over one page for 10 seconds without taking your pencil off.

Then do this again three more times but start in a different place on the page each time.

Colour in the shapes that get formed from the squiggles and make a beautiful, random pattern design, or see if you can make a picture from the different shapes.

Help Bob find new and exciting opportunities from a page that just looks like squiggles at first.

CHALLENGE: CAN YOU SEE ANY OF THESE THINGS IN YOUR SQUIGGLE PAGE? YOU MIGHT HAVE TO USE YOUR IMAGINATION A BIT!

A smiling face

A football

A cat

An alien

A cuddly toy

RAINBOW

Having more time to notice things can be a really positive experience.

COPY THIS RAINBOW DESIGN ON A PIECE OF PAPER, OR DESIGN YOUR OWN.

Colour it in and put it in the window, on your mirror, the fridge door or wherever it will make you and other people remember that beautiful things happen in difficult times.

Rain breaks up sunlight into different colours so you can see them all clearly. You don't get rainbows to enjoy unless there's rain. Use this time to remember all the things you have in your life to enjoy now or to look forward to in the future.

If you prefer, you could tear up old magazines or coloured paper into small pieces and glue them onto the rainbow to give it an extra something! Always ask permission before cutting anything up and ask for help when using scissors.

KEEP CALM!

Write and illustrate an acrostic poem to help others KEEP CALM! during this time.

You could send it to your loved ones, learn it by heart, record yourself performing or reading it, turn it into a song or a meme or ask an adult to put it on social media for your family to enjoy.

Make sure the first word in each line starts with the capital letter for that line. You can make the capital letter extra big and decorate it too, if you like.

Poems can rhyme but they don't have to – write your poem exactly how you want it to be!

IDEAS FOR WHAT TO INCLUDE IN YOUR POEM:

- tips from this book for keeping calm
- reminders to be positive
- encouragement for people to help each other

- noticing the things that are better at the moment like less pollution and more wildlife
- a snappy 'call to action' such as 'never give up!'

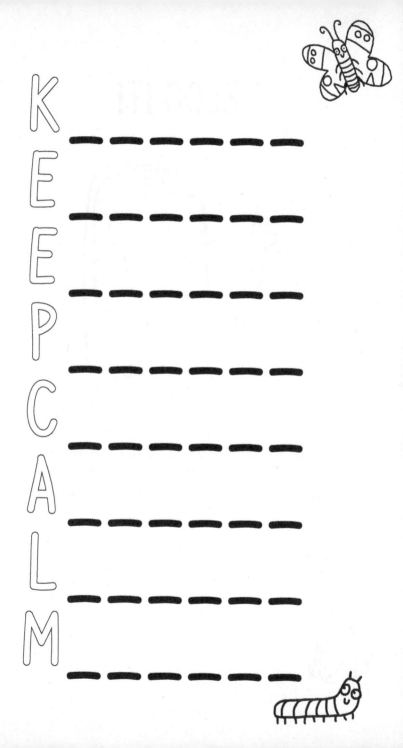

BLOG IT!

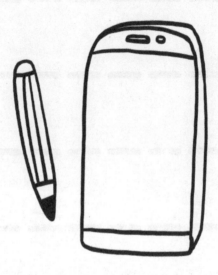

Living through history is very exciting – even the boring bits will be interesting to other people and you'll have lots of fascinating stories to tell younger people when you're older.

Keep a record of these events now in a blog or diary.

You don't have to write about the big things.
As well as learning how situations and events made you
feel, people love to know what everyday life was like.

What time you get up, what you have for meals, where
you go on walks, how it feels to do schoolwork at home,
what games you play, all make good stories as well as any
funny tales about making or doing new things for the first time.

Who are you going to share your blog with?

Can you encourage others to keep a
blog as well and compare your stories?

PASS IT ON

When things get a bit overwhelming, they often seem much bigger than they really are and sometimes things just feel too big for us to deal with by ourselves. You don't have to manage everything by yourself - you can pass it on to an adult and KEEP CALM!

Write down the three most difficult things for you right now.

List under each one what you can do to get it sorted out. If you don't know what to do, ask an adult to help you find the solution. You'll be glad you did.

Sometimes, there is no immediate solution but you can still feel better if you pass it on. Why not try a Talk12 or a High Five?

If you don't need this activity right now, save it up until you do!

Make sure you tell your friends they can PASS IT ON, too.

Here are some top tips to help you deal with huge thoughts – don't forget to come up with your own as well:

Focus on what's important

Make a list

Have a huge hug

Find five beautiful things that you can see, hear, touch, smell or taste

Tell someone

Talk to someone for 12 minutes about anything you like – comics, books, hobbies, sports, fashion, animals, music and films all make for good conversations.

TALK
12

HIGH FIVE

1. Eat for health.

2. Drink water.

3. Get plenty of exercise.

4. Get enough rest and sleep.

5. Make sure you find time every day to do things you enjoy with people who care about you.

WHEN I NEED YOU

It isn't always easy to remember what you need to help you KEEP CALM!, especially when Bob is barking at you and giving you lots of feelings to manage. It's always best to be prepared so you can quickly get what you need with no fuss! This will be a treat for Bob and will train him not to kick off.

Use pieces of paper, sticky notes, blank playing cards or homemade cut-out shapes from old greetings cards or packaging to make a set of cards that will help you ask for what you need when you're not feeling great. Write these words onto your cards, putting in the missing information that works for you.

Make as many others as you want to cover all the feelings you can think of. Every time you notice a new feeling, make a card for it and add it to your set.

Next time Bob starts yapping, grab your cards, remind yourself what you need and get it! You can show the card to an adult to help explain what's happening and what you need.

Encourage others in your family to make their own set.

I NEED
a snack

**I'M UPSET,
I NEED**
a hug

**I'M CROSS,
I NEED**
some time alone

**I'M BORED,
I NEED**
*to hear
something lovely*

I NEED
reassurance

I FEEL

I'M

**I'M HAPPY,
I NEED**

I NEED
a hug

KEEP CALM! JAR

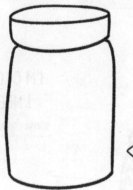

Find an empty jar with a lid –
pick one you like the shape of
if there is a choice of jars.
Wash and dry it thoroughly.

Decorate it with pens,
magazine pictures, ribbons, stickers
or anything you have available.

Make a label for it.

Keep your jar somewhere you can see it every day.

Every time you have a lovely memory or get a compliment, do something really well or feel grateful, write it down on a slip of paper or a sticky note, fold it up and put it safely in the jar.

I played my trombone when everyone clapped for the NHS

My teacher said my home school project was really good

I am thankful that I can still talk to Grandma on the phone

Whenever you're feeling upset, worried or unhappy, just grab your jar and read all the messages until you feel calm and can carry on again.

Bob will love listening to all those positive messages and will know he isn't the only one looking out for you.

BREATHE CALM

If you are feeling uncomfortable, upset or
overwhelmed, you can do this activity anywhere,
anytime and enjoy breathing to KEEP CALM!

Take yourself
somewhere peaceful
and sit still
and quietly.

If you have a private
outdoors space, you could
find a quiet spot outside.
You are part of nature.

Pay attention to your breathing
for a few minutes. Imagine you are
breathing in calm and breathing
out hurt, like your upset or
other negative feelings.

CALM

FEAR

Now start 3:5 breathing. Breathe
in for a count of three, and then
slowly out for a count of five.
Keep this going for a few minutes
until you start to feel relaxed.

This works wherever you are and whatever you are doing. The best part is that no one will know you're doing it, so if you need to boost your inner positivity without being noticed, give it a try.

Get comfortable, in a sitting position. Notice your body breathing in and out.

After a few breaths, start to count along with yourself, making your in-breath last for the count of three and your out-breath last for the count of five, breathing smoothly.

Keep going for as long you want to, or until you feel great.

Next, imagine a place where you could feel totally safe and comfortable and the world is calm. Draw it with lots of detail or stick in a picture from a magazine or a photo.

Spend five minutes staring at your picture and make a mind movie of you being there feeling great!

Your safe place could be somewhere you've seen or been to, heard about, read about or dreamed about. A special, safe place where everything feels peaceful, calm and safe.

3 TIMES CALMER

When you need a quick way to KEEP CALM!, breathing mindfully does the job!
Teach these skills to someone else to help spread the word to anyone who
might need to know about them. You could show your family and friends
how to do these during video chats and help them feel better, too!

Get into a comfortable position, laying down or sitting if you prefer.
Start 3:5 breathing. Pay attention to your surroundings, wherever you
happen to be. Make a list in your head of three things you can hear.
Let each one go before you listen for the next one.

Then make a list in your head of three things you can see.
Again, let each one fade before looking for the next thing.

Now, tune into your body and find three things you can feel, like your
heart beating or the breeze on your face or perhaps a blanket or the
floor underneath you. Let each one pass on before noticing the next one.

TRIANGLE BREATHING

works well too.
Run your finger along one side of a triangle as you do each of these until you've made a complete triangle.

1. DEEP, SLOW BREATH IN
2. HOLD AND SMILE
3. DEEP, SLOW BREATH OUT

1. Breathe in
2. Hold your breath and smile
3. Breathe out

Do this as many times as you want. You can trace triangles on your palm, a desk, your lap or anything else that's handy.

FINGER BREATHING

Spread your hand out. Use your pointer finger and put it on the bottom knuckle of your opposite thumb. Slowly and smoothly trace it up your thumb, breathing in as you do.

Stop at the tip, hold your breath for a second, then trace back down the other side as you breathe out. Trace every finger in the same way. Remember to keep your breathing smooth too. Repeat this a few times, and make sure all your attention is on your hand and your breath.

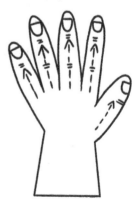

Bob often falls asleep when you're three times calmer!

SOUND IT OUT

Is it noisy or quiet where you are? Have you ever stopped to notice the sounds around you? Now's the time to really listen to your world.

You can do this indoors or outdoors, wherever you are.

You could do it when you go for a walk, but make sure to follow advice about social distancing.

If you have your own yard or garden, you could rest here for a few minutes. Take off your shoes and socks and let the air get to your toes if you can.

Get comfy, close your eyes and just listen. Try to follow the sounds without working out what they are or where they are coming from.

Try to resist judging them in any way, just enjoy them exactly as they are.

Use 3:5 breathing while you do this to give yourself a proper treat!

KEEP CALM! KIT

Make your very own calming kit to
help you cope with what's happening.

Any time you need a boost
of calm, grab your kit and
enjoy chilling out with it.

Find something you can recycle to use for this –
an old shoe box, lunchbox, ice-cream box or gift bag would work well.

Or use your own ideas to create a suitable container.

DECORATE IT HOWEVER YOU WISH.

YOU COULD USE:

Coloured paper

Paint

Glue or tape

Pens

Pictures of your
favourite characters

Magazines

Decorations like buttons,
ribbons or stickers

Fill your container with items you like to look at, smell, taste, touch or listen to or that have special memories for you.

HERE ARE SOME IDEAS:

Soft toys

Rubber bands

Material

Modelling clay

Fidget toys

Worry stones

Old tickets

Stress ball

Hand lotion

Old birthday cards

Beads

Pompoms

Friendship bracelets

Music

Bubble wrap

Fabric with scent

Photo of someone you love

Small pack of sweets

Mirror

HAPPY HISTORY CAPSULE

These are historic times so why not make your own historical artefact to let future generations find out about your life in the time of coronavirus and the coronavirus pandemic?

Create a time capsule to record what you like and how things are for you today. You might enjoy looking back to this time from the future!

YOU WILL NEED:

A large jar or plastic container

An old plastic bag

Collection of information about yourself, photos and memorabilia

INSTRUCTIONS:

Put your information and small objects into the jar or container. Seal it up.

Decide where you're going to store your capsule. You could put it at the back of your wardrobe or wrap it in the plastic bag and bury it in the garden.

Don't forget to write down where it is so you can find it again, and make sure to ask an adult first!

You could record all kinds of information about yourself such as your name, age, address, school, teacher, best friends and height.

Maybe you'd like to include all the things you want to do when the pandemic is over and life has gone back to normal.

Ask other people at home to add something as well, if you like.

How about adding a list of your favourite things?

Song artists	Games	Movies	YouTubers
Songs	Hobbies	Celebrities	Sports teams
Foods	Toys	School subjects	Colours
	Books		

Other information you might include:

Top three family memories with photos

A letter from your family

A letter to yourself or future generations about what you've been doing

Tips for home schooling

Wish list for the future

Funny stories from your family's experiences e.g. a lockdown birthday

Favourite words and expressions

Magazine pictures of fashions popular right now

Top three moments during the pandemic

SAY IT AGAIN!

Sometimes you can get stuck in a negative mood and you might feel rubbish about what is happening right now.

Everyone experiences this from time to time.

If it happens to you or someone you care about, try using the SAY IT AGAIN machine to look at things in a more positive way.

Focus on what you do have and can do, rather than what's missing.

Write down some things you say when you're feeling negative and put them through the machine to see what comes out!

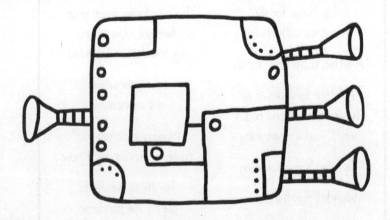

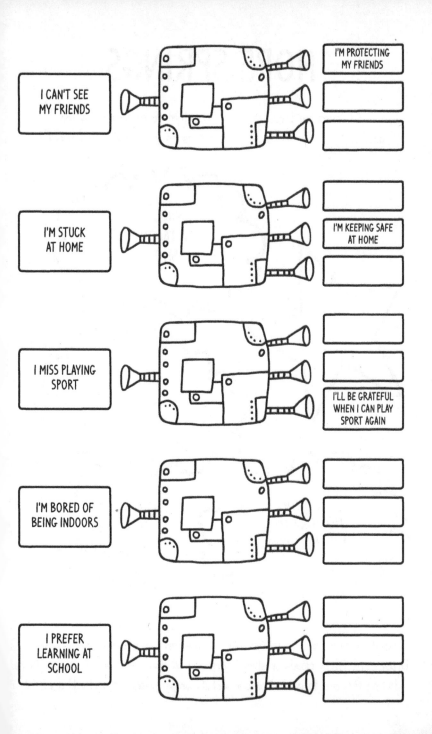

I CAN'T SEE MY FRIENDS

I'M PROTECTING MY FRIENDS

I'M STUCK AT HOME

I'M KEEPING SAFE AT HOME

I MISS PLAYING SPORT

I'LL BE GRATEFUL WHEN I CAN PLAY SPORT AGAIN

I'M BORED OF BEING INDOORS

I PREFER LEARNING AT SCHOOL

HOPE SPRINGS

At times like these, it's very important to remember all the good things in the world and all the reasons you have to feel hopeful.

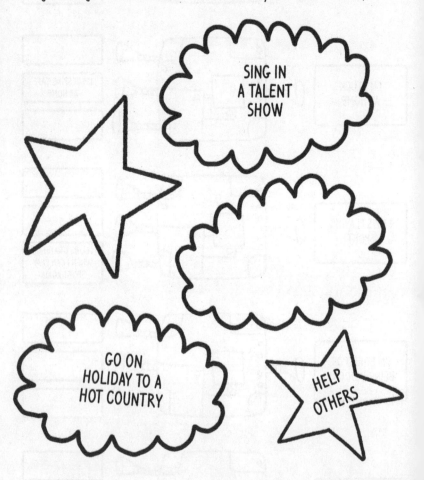

SING IN A TALENT SHOW

GO ON HOLIDAY TO A HOT COUNTRY

HELP OTHERS

What exciting things would you like to do when things are back to normal? Draw some fluffy clouds or shiny stars and fill them with all the things you're looking forward to doing. You can include simple pleasures and wild dreams!

When you have a quiet moment, look out of the window or go outside if you can. Look up at the sky and watch the clouds moving or the stars shining.

Pick a few of your hopes and make a mind movie of those things happening.

Notice how you feel while they are happening in your mind.

ROSETTES

Draw some rosettes on paper and cut them out.

You could also use card from the recycling, printed sheets, magazines and ribbons if you have them. You can award them to people in your home or community, in person or by sending a photo if you can't visit them.

GOOD LISTENER

KEY WORKER

POSITIVE PERSON

Write their names on the ribbons and why they have been awarded the rosette in the circle.

HELPFUL

WHAT A
WONDERFUL WORLD

It's time to notice everything that is wonderful, amazing and beautiful in your world. Look out of the window, sit outside if you can and just look.

Draw a circle and fill it with all the wonderful people and things you can see, hear, smell, touch and taste.

MY INCREDIBLE WORLD IS FULL OF WONDERFUL THINGS AND PEOPLE

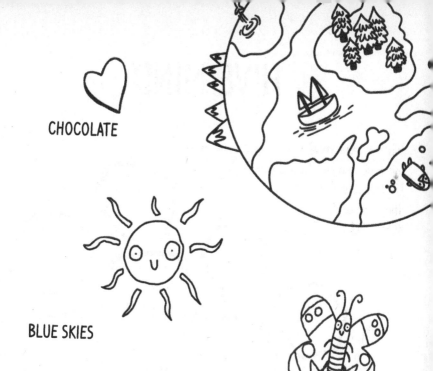

CHOCOLATE

BLUE SKIES

FLOWERS

MY FAMILY

MUSIC

HIVE MIND

Who's in your hive? We all need people in
our lives who just fit and who make
life feel as sweet as honey.
They help us to
KEEP CALM!

MY
BROTHER

MY
TEACHER

GRANDMA

MY BEST
FRIEND

Draw your hive,
putting each person in
their own section of honeycomb.
Choose people from your family,
friends, clubs and anywhere else.

SAY WHAT?

Write these words onto a piece of paper, decorate it with colours and drawings and turn it into a window poster to keep everyone in your community feeling supported.

WE'VE GOT THIS!

PASSING THROUGH

Draw this onto a piece of paper, decorate it with colours and doodles and turn it into a window poster to keep everyone in your community feeling supported.

THIS WILL PASS

CALM CHAT

This chatterbox game is a great way to remind people how to KEEP CALM!

Write messages under the flaps that people will find comforting or remind them of tips for staying calm. You can choose an adult or friend to do this with or just keep it for when you need a KEEP CALM! reminder.

YOU WILL NEED:
A4 paper, scissors, pens or crayons

(Ask an adult to help you when using scissors.)

INSTRUCTIONS:
Turn your sheet of paper into a square:

A. Fold the top corner down to make a triangle

B. Cut off the spare rectangle under the triangle

C. Unfold the triangle to get a square

1. Fold paper diagonally making 4 identical triangles and open it.

2. Fold each corner to the centre of the sheet of paper to make a smaller square.

3. Turn it over, fold each corner to the centre, making an even smaller square.

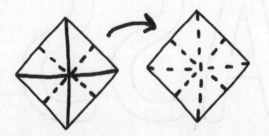

4. Fold your square in half both ways.

5. Open the pockets behind each square and put your fingers into the spaces.

6. Open and close each way just by moving your fingers!

7. Colour the 4 outer squares in different colours.

8. Write a number from 1-8 on each of the 8 inner triangles.

9. Behind each of these triangles, write a calming reminder for yourself or others.

LET'S PLAY!

Ask for a colour from your 4 choices and spell it, opening the chatterbox once for each letter – so if it's B-L-U-E, open it 4 times, first one way, then the next.

Ask for a number on display. Open the chatterbox this many times, first one way, then the next.

Ask for another number on display, lift up the flap and read your message!

OUT OF THE BLUE

When people suddenly started to become ill with COVID-19 and we had to stay at home, it probably felt like a shock to you and your family.

SHOCK

You've probably missed out on some important events since it started, like saying goodbye to school friends and teachers or celebrating special events. It's OK to be upset about this - you need to come to terms with the shock and let it go.

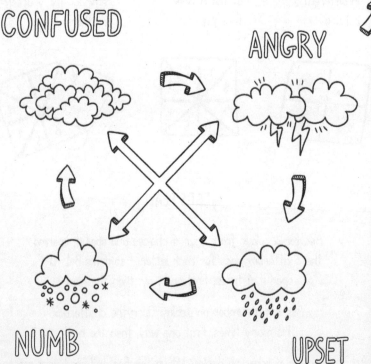

CONFUSED

ANGRY

NUMB

UPSET

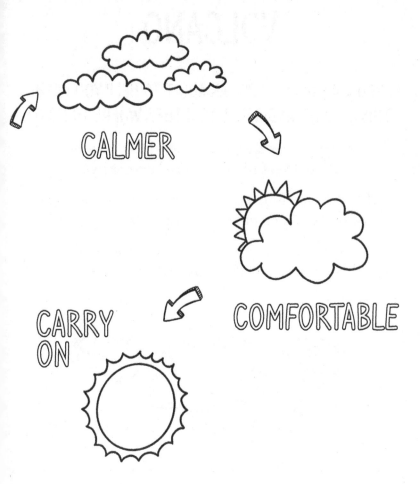

Use this diagram to make sense of your
feelings and talk it through with someone.

Explain how you feel about each section. Then listen to
their explanations and then have a big hug together.

VOLCANO

YOU WILL NEED TO ASK AN ADULT TO HELP YOU WITH THIS ACTIVITY AND AGREE TOGETHER WHERE TO DO IT!

Feeling uncertain about when life will get back to normal can make you (and others at home) super stressed.

When that stress builds up for a while, it can make you feel angry and irritable. Why not put all that feeling into making a volcano?

This activity will help you let off steam in the garden, kitchen sink or bath in a safe and exciting way!

YOU WILL NEED:

Plasticine or papier maché to make the volcano casing (optional)

Clean container e.g. a plastic beaker, jar, water bottle, washing-up bottle, shampoo bottle, used tin or drinks can

Vinegar, mixing bowl, washing-up liquid, 2 drops red food colouring (optional), tablespoon of baking soda/ sodium bicarbonate, tissue or kitchen roll, elastic band

INSTRUCTIONS:

If you want to make a plasticine or papier maché volcano casing, put the container on a flat surface and make a cone-shaped casing around it.

Wait for it to dry if needed.

Mix the vinegar with red food colouring and a tablespoon of washing-up liquid in a bowl.

Pour the mixture into the container.

Put the baking soda/sodium bicarbonate onto a tissue or kitchen roll and make a small sausage shape with it, holding it closed with an elastic band.

Make sure it is narrower than the opening of your volcano.

NOW DROP THIS INTO YOUR CONTAINER AND STAND WELL BACK!

GIVE ME YOUR HAND

KEEP CALM! WE'RE ALL IN THIS TOGETHER!

Everyone in your home is going through this with you.

Family and friends who live in a different home are all going
through it too. It's important to give each other a helping hand.

Create a special artwork for your home that you can frame so
you will always remember how you all helped each other out through
this unusual time. You could make several copies and turn this artwork
into a card to send to your loved ones to support them as well.

YOU WILL NEED:

Paper, thin card, wrapping paper,   Scissors   Glue
coloured paper or plain paper

Ask each person at home to choose a piece of paper. If you have
any wrapping paper, this works very well as does any paper or
thin card you have in the recycling but plain paper is good, too.

Draw round each person's hand on their chosen piece of paper and cut it out.

Take another piece of paper or thin card and stick the largest hand onto it.

Keep sticking the hands on, one on top of the other, making sure
that they go in size order, so the smallest will be on the top.

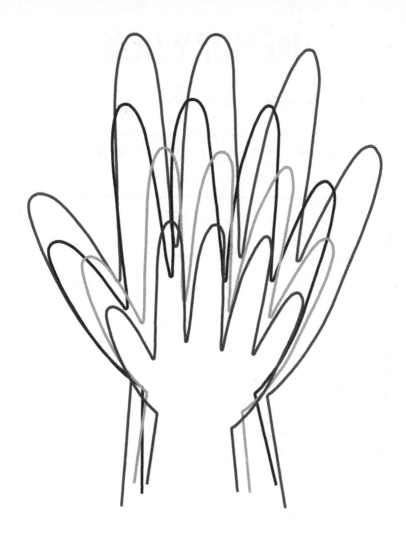

You could write your names on the hands or just leave them as they are. You could write the date underneath the hands if you like.

Scan into the computer or take a photo in case you want to send out cards with your artwork. You could give your artwork a title or description too.

Frame, put up on the wall and enjoy!

MEMORY BOX

A memory box is a great way to celebrate a person or pet you love.

You can use it to keep special things that remind you
of them and the relationship you have or had together.

YOU WILL NEED:

Cardboard box
with a lid

Coloured paper

Paint

Glue stick/tape

Pens

A picture of your
loved one

Scissors

Magazines

Decorations like
buttons, ribbon,
stickers

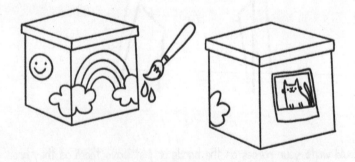

Paint or cover your box with paper – perhaps
in your special person's favourite colour.

Put a photo on the box and add any pictures and words you
want to put on the box, too. Decorate the box however you like.

Use your memory box to keep all your memories in one place and look through it when you want to feel close to them.

THINGS TO INCLUDE:

Their favourite scent

Music that was important to you both

Anything that reminds you of them

Cuddly toy

Old tickets

Cards from birthdays and other special occasions

Photos

When you think of a special memory, you could write it on a piece of notepaper and add it to the box, too.

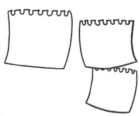

LAUGH IT OUT

Jessica and Harry love to tell jokes and laugh at each other's impersonations of animals and famous people.

Bob thinks laughing is the best cure for any problem!

Do you know any good jokes?

Write some down (and look up a few others) and plan a time with your family when you can crack them up with your comedy show.

You could even video call people who cannot be there in person.

Get everyone involved – take it in turns to impersonate
an animal, a cartoon character or a famous person.

You can use sticky notes or scraps of paper to write the
names of the animals, characters and celebrities and put these
into a jar or envelope for people to pull out and perform!

You can all try to guess who they are trying to be!

HERE ARE SOME ANIMAL IDEAS TO START YOU OFF:

alligator	elephant	kangaroo	seagull
bird	fish	lion	seal
butterfly	frog	monkey	shark
cat	giraffe	mouse	snake
chimpanzee	grizzly bear	owl	turtle
dog	hamster	penguin	
duck	hedgehog	rabbit	

FESTIVAL OF HOME

You can involve all the family in this one!
Don't forget you can use video chat platforms
to spread the joy even further.

Ask everyone to think of something they can do to amuse
or entertain the whole family – including pets and soft toys –
for an afternoon, evening or whole weekend, outdoors
(if you have a garden or outdoor space) or indoors.

Acts could include singing, dancing, reading, magic tricks, reciting poetry, playing the spoons, burping the alphabet – anything goes as long as it's fun for all the family!

Make sure you end your festival with everyone doing the same thing together – like singing your favourite song or having a dance.

PLANNING TIPS

Decide on a date and time.

Ask an adult to announce it on social media to the family group.

Make paper/card bunting using the
materials from the recycling box.

Put up fairy lights.

Make tickets for everyone.

Make wristbands from scraps of paper and sticky tape
for people to wear so they feel like it's a festival!

Invite your wider family and friends to attend
and maybe even participate through video chat.

Get the snacks and drinks lined up.

Set up the camera to record or connect.

Get dressed up and attend your very own Festival of Home!

HANDS TOGETHER

To keep coronavirus out of your body, it's important to try to make sure you don't touch your eyes, nose or mouth so use a clean tissue every time you need to blow your nose, cough or sneeze and put it straight into the bin.

Then wash your hands for 20 seconds. If you don't have a tissue, you can sneeze or cough into the inside of your elbow. When you do need to touch any part of your face, that's OK – just give your hands a wash first and then again afterwards. You can also use hand sanitiser if you can't wash your hands.

Washing your hands for 20 seconds is important – why not find songs that take 20 seconds to sing, like Happy Birthday sung twice?

Or you could make up a very silly song and use that each time (check that it takes 20 seconds!).

Wet your hands with
warm running water.

Turn off the tap to preserve
water for the environment.

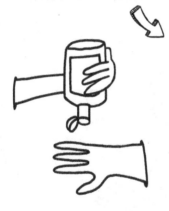

Add soap to your hands

Rub them together with the
soap and bubble them up.

Rub the backs of your
hands, wrists, between your
fingers, and under your nails.

Keep doing this for
20 seconds then
turn on the tap.

Rinse your hands well
under running water.

Dry your hands using a clean
towel or let the air dry them.

HANDLE WITH CARE

After washing your hands, it's a good idea to use some hand cream. Make sure the lid is firmly closed and wash the outside of the hand cream pot or bottle with soap and water or sanitiser before you use it.

Ask an adult to wash their hands with you and then get some hand cream with a great smell. Smell the cream together and enjoy the scent for a few seconds, saying what it reminds you of, why you like it and anything else you notice about it.

Decide who will go first and spend five minutes massaging this cream really well all over the other person's hands, making sure to gently cover every part and to take notice of how it feels.

Remind yourselves that you are helping each other to stay safe and feel loved and protected.

After five minutes, swap over.

Do this activity once a day together. You can do this activity with different family members as well so you share the love.

YOU WILL NEED

An adult   Some lovely hand cream

A towel   10 minutes of your time

Safety warning: ask the adult to make sure the cream is safe for you to use

Bob loves this activity – it really soothes him and helps him to relax. It gives him soft paws, too!

WORLDLY GOODS

During the pandemic, there have also been very good things happening across the world.

Nature seems to be flourishing.

There has been far less pollution for our planet to deal with which has made our air healthier. Because of this, the sky is clearer and we can see the stars more clearly at night.

Animals have been seen in places they don't usually go because there are fewer people.

There is more time to relax and do fun things like chatting, reading and drawing activities!

What other good things have you noticed or heard about that are happening during this time?

Make three lists and separate your ideas into these headings:

PEOPLE

PLACES

NATURE

Perhaps we can learn from this and when things go back to normal, we can all help to make a new and better normal where all these good things can stay.

Make a pledge to help create a new and better normal and say what you will do differently to make it happen.

Remember, you are NEVER too small to make a difference!

I, _____,

PLEDGE TO _____

_____

TO HELP CREATE A NEW, BETTER NORMAL FOR THE WORLD.

SIGNED _____

DATE _____

Copy this pledge onto a piece of paper, add your name, what you're going to do, your signature and the date, and then display your pledge in your home.

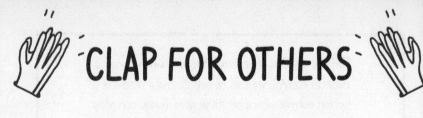

CLAP FOR OTHERS

In some countries, people have been standing on their balcony or doorstep regularly to thank people in the community who have been working hard to look after everybody else.

These people include shop and care workers, medical and school staff, police and military workers, builders, engineers, drivers, postal workers and many others.

Who would you like to clap for?

Design a banner to say thank you to them. Make sure your banner says who you are thanking and why. You could put this in your window, hold it up whilst everyone claps or give or send it to the person or people you're thinking of.

CLAP FOR YOU!

You deserve a clap, too!

Your world has been turned upside down for a while.

You've had to make huge changes and give up
things you love while this has been going on.

What would you like people to recognise
as your contribution during this time?

Staying home until it's over is a vital
contribution as it stops the virus from
spreading. Getting back to normal life will also
be a vital contribution when the time comes.

Imagine hearing everyone clapping for you and
feel super proud of yourself – you should be!
Bob is super proud of you.

Why not ask everyone at home why they deserve
a clap and make a banner for each of them?
You could have a special time every day when you all give
yourselves a 30 second clap together to help you keep going.

If you can keep going, you can KEEP CALM!

BANK IT UP

Keeping a record of the ways people have helped you is
a good way of remembering to say thank you when
life returns to normal. Feeling that others care
about you is a great way to learn to KEEP CALM!

Find a clean jar with or without a lid.
Use marker pens, magazine pictures or
acrylic paint to decorate it like a piggy bank.

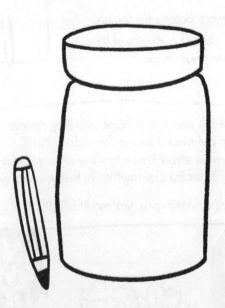

Every time someone does something kind for you, helps you or sorts something out for you, write it on a slip of paper or a sticky note together with their name and pop it in your jar. If you find something in this book helpful, write that down and pop it in your jar, too!

That way you'll remember to use it to KEEP CALM! in the future as well.

When the pandemic is over, take your jar and sit down with a pile of paper or card and write to each person to give them a heartfelt thank you for helping you to KEEP CALM!

Make sure you also say thank you at the time whenever someone supports you!

RING THE BELL

When the pandemic is over and life is back to normal,
you might want to celebrate and mark it with a special event.

We will reach that day and it will feel amazing!

Make a mind movie of how you and everyone else will react

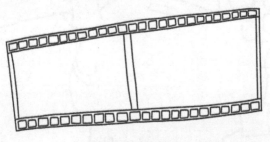

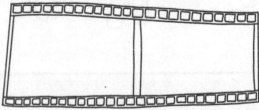

Until then, you can imagine ringing a bell whenever you need to
feel a bit of comfort. Draw yourself a bell and colour it in.

You could draw a bell each time you need some comfort –
why not create lots of different designs?

Listen to your bell ringing – how loud is it?

Is it high or low pitched?

How long does it ding for?

What does it remind you of?

Now picture all your friends and family
ringing the bell together.

What a terrific feeling and sight that is!

You could make a bell picture for everyone
you love, send it to them and show them what
to do to keep their minds focused on the end of
this time in history and going back to normal life.

UNDER THE SAME SKY

Everyone you love, all the animals you admire and everything that grows all live under the same sky. The sky you are under right now.

Copy this landscape, or design your own, and draw all the things you want to celebrate in the world under the sky.

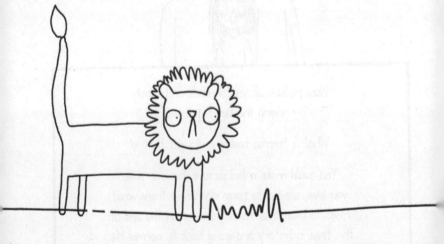

Notice how connected you are to all these things.

Feeling connected helps you to KEEP CALM!

The world will return to normal one day soon.

Until then, bring it all a bit closer to you.

CALM YOGA

You are a warrior who's already overcome lots of difficulties.

You've got this! Let's help your inner warrior to KEEP CALM! with some yoga poses so you can carry on through this time with confidence.

WARRIOR 1

Stand straight then step forward with your front knee bent, your back leg straight behind you. Arch your back, stretch your arms and hands up to the sky. Look straight ahead.

Say 'I am strong'.

WARRIOR 2

From Warrior 1, stretch your arms out in front
of you and turn your chest. Have one arm stretched
forward and the other stretched behind you.

Say 'I am powerful'.

WARRIOR 3

From Warrior 2, bring both your arms in front of you
and straighten your front leg. Lift your back foot off the
ground a little. Open your arms for balance if needed.

Say 'I am brave'.

Feeling calm, yet?

You can also help Bob feel supported with these animal poses.

If he isn't the only one protecting you, he can relax a little!

TURTLE POSE

Stretch your legs to the sides. With your knees bent, push your head and tummy forward and tuck your hands under your ankles.

Say 'I choose calm'.

MOUSE POSE

Kneel on the floor with your feet together.
Lower your chest onto your thighs and your chin onto your
knees with your arms and hands by your sides, palms up.

Say 'I am safe
and protected'.

LION POSE

Stay kneeling on the floor and put your feet together.
Place your hands on your knees or the floor in front,
arch your back and lift your head. Stretch out
your tongue as if you are roaring.

Say 'I am brave'.

MINDFUL MOUTHS

This experiment helps you to really notice what happens when you eat and keeps your mind focused on the moment.

You can do this with the whole family or with an adult.

YOU WILL NEED

one raisin and one you!

HERE'S WHAT TO DO

Sit comfortably and take two or three comfortable deep breaths.

Place the raisin in your hand.

Look closely at the raisin and with your full attention imagine that it's like something you've never seen before in your life.

Now close your eyes. Place the raisin on one of your fingers and gently move it around on your hand, exploring it carefully.

What does the raisin feel like?

Hold the raisin near your nose and notice its smell.
Does anything interesting happen in your mouth or tummy?

Slowly bring the raisin up to your lips
then rub it across your lips and notice
what that feels like. It might feel
difficult not to just pop it in your mouth.

Put the raisin on your tongue and let it
sit there for a few seconds. Don't chew it.

Just leave it on your tongue
and notice how it feels.

Now very slowly begin to chew it.
Bite it gently and notice what it
feels like between your teeth.

Don't swallow it just yet. Wait until the taste
fills your mouth, then swallow it down.

Notice your breathing again
and then open your eyes.

If you don't like raisins, use a blueberry, raspberry,
blackcurrant, orange segment or a very small piece of chocolate.
Make sure it's something you're not allergic to!

MANDALA
MAGIC

Copy or trace these mandalas, then colour them in and let the calm wash over you as you do!

COPY AND
COLOUR

I
AM
CALM

TAKE IT IN

Spending time outside is really good for your brain and body.

It can slow your heart rate, reduce stress and develop your world view because you can't help noticing how amazing the world is. YOU are part of the world and you're amazing too!

When you are able to go outside for exercise, take some time to do this activity with someone in your family or by yourself as you have a short rest. If you can't go outside, look out of a window and do it from there instead.

Make sure the window is secured so you are safe.

Start by looking down. Find a living, growing or moving natural thing like an insect, a flower, a blade of grass or whatever you like. Don't catch it or pick it – respect its right to be free and alive.

Sit or lay down and focus on watching your natural thing for 1 or 2 minutes (or longer if you like).

Don't do anything except notice the thing you are looking at.

Look at it as if you are seeing it for the very first time ever.

Find two more things to observe and repeat the activity with those things.

When you've finished, notice the way you're feeling and describe it in writing or draw how you feel.

Find something natural that has fallen from a tree, plant or animal like a leaf, flower or feather and take it home.

Wash your hands when you get in and wash your natural treasure as well if it's possible. Place it somewhere you can see it and touch it, and where Bob can enjoy it.

INVISIBLE STRING

EVEN WHEN YOU ARE SEPARATED FROM PEOPLE YOU LOVE, THEY STILL LOVE YOU. YOU ARE NOT ALONE!

Your heart is joined to the hearts of everyone you love and everyone who loves you by an invisible string. You always carry their love in your heart wherever you are, and whatever you are doing. If someone is no longer alive, they still count because your hearts were connected.

Draw a heart and write your name in it.

Draw some more hearts on the page and write the
names of everyone you're joined to by the invisible string.

Add even more hearts if you like.

If your connected hearts are in different parts of the world, you could
make a note on the world map to show how far your love travels.

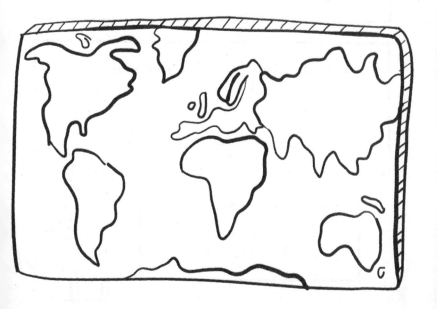

SCHEDULE IT!

If you love a plan and like knowing what is coming up with schoolwork, rest time, chores, activities and exercise time, then sit down with an adult and agree a schedule for your days spent at home.

Chat through what you want to get done each day and the things that are important to you like having time to chill out, chat to friends, go on devices, have a cuddle, read, play and be with your family. Decide if the schedule will be different on weekdays and weekends.

Make a list of the things that you want to include on your schedule. Agree how much time you can spend on each thing and then draw up the schedule together.

Put it up somewhere everyone can see it!

Now, you know what you're doing, Bob will KEEP CALM!

BEFORE 9 AM	WAKE UP	Eat breakfast, make your bed, put PJs in the laundry.
9 AM – 10 AM	MORNING WALK	Family walk with the dog, or yoga
10 AM – 11 AM	SCHOOL TIME	No electronics. Sudoku, flash cards, study guide, journal
11 AM – 12 PM	CREATIVE TIME	Drawing, crafting, playing music, cooking or baking.
12 PM	LUNCH	Lunch
12:30 PM	CHORE TIME	e.g. wipe door handles, switches and worktops.
1 PM – 2:30 PM	QUIET TIME	Reading, puzzles and a nap.
2:30 PM – 4 PM	SCHOOL TIME	Electronics OK. Tablet games, educational shows.
4 PM – 5 PM	FRESH AIR	Play in the garden.
5 PM – 6 PM	DINNER	Dinner
6 PM – 8 PM	FREE TV TIME	
8 PM	BEDTIME	
9 PM	BEDTIME	

LETTER LOVE

Life is usually very busy so it's not as common to send and receive letters as it used to be. Older family members and friends especially love getting happy letters.

Younger family members would probably love getting them as well!

Would you like to send someone a handwritten letter and receive one back in return? You might start a new trend!

YOU COULD WRITE ABOUT:

- things you've been doing during the pandemic

- things you've learnt that you didn't know before

- what you are most looking forward to doing again

- what you're going to do differently in future

- things you've enjoyed

- things you've found boring

- things that have surprised you

- funny, sad or interesting things that have happened

- how important they are to you

- how you'll feel to see them again

YOU COULD WRITE TO:

- Grandparents
- Aunts and Uncles
- Cousins
- Friends from school
- Friends from clubs
- Neighbours
- Anyone else you miss seeing

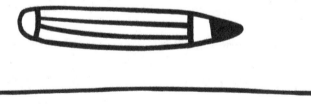

Go on, you'll make someone's day with a lovely letter –
and if you ask for a reply, they might just make your day, too!

INDOOR
TREASURE HUNT

Make copies of these treasure hunt lists for your family and then get hunting for these items! You could set a time limit and see who has the most items collected before time runs out.

Alternatively, you could keep going until someone has the whole set.

INDOOR LIST

A fork	A key
Something red	Two matching socks
A tissue box	Something square
Three things with wheels	A sticker
An orange crayon	A pair of glasses
Something very soft	An envelope

OUTDOOR
TREASURE HUNT

You can decide on the rules for this treasure hunt as well.

Whatever you decide, make sure everyone
knows not to pick anything – they can just
tick off the item and say where it was.

OUTDOOR LIST

Two kinds of leaves	Something green and growing
Something yellow	A bird
Three sticks	Something purple
Something that smells good	A bug
Something in the sky	A pebble
Something round	A flower

HEART OF THE MATTER

Draw a huge heart.

Fill it with everyone you love and who loves you.
Include pets and favourite soft toys too if you like.

You are so loved!

MAKING MEMORIES

When all this is over, you might quickly forget the old, long-gone pandemic days.

Make some memories now of the best times so you can share and laugh about them in the future.

Whenever something feels good, stop and take a selfie!

You could draw it, too and even add the date and a quick description of what you were doing and why it was so much fun.

SHADOW DRAWINGS

When the sun shines, shadows appear on the ground or walls.

Put a toy animal somewhere it will form a shadow with the sun shining on it. Place some paper behind it – if you're using a wall, use a bit of sticky-tac to keep the paper still but check with an adult before sticking anything!

If you're using the ground, use a book or a tray to create a hard surface to make sure you get a good drawing.

Move your toy until you are happy with the shadow and then draw around the shadow onto the paper.

Repeat with the same or other animals.

You can create a whole jungle, dinosaur park or teddy bear's picnic – or mix it up and create a teddy bear's jungle, dinosaur picnic or... well, whatever you like!

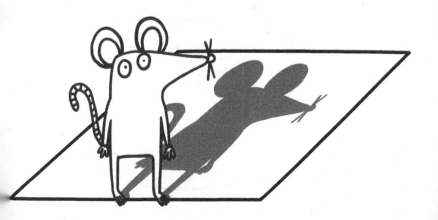

BUBBLE TIME

Fancy letting your worries pop off to
help you KEEP CALM!? It's bubble time!

Draw yourself in a huge bubble.
Make sure you look relaxed, happy and comfy.

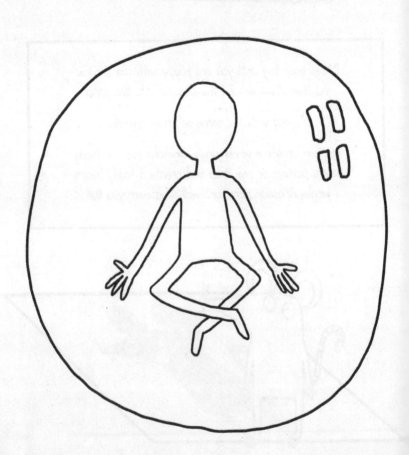

Add little bubbles around the big bubble for your worries –
colour them, label them or leave them blank as you wish.

Make the outside of your big bubble really
thick and use your favourite colours.

Colour inside the bubble if you want to.

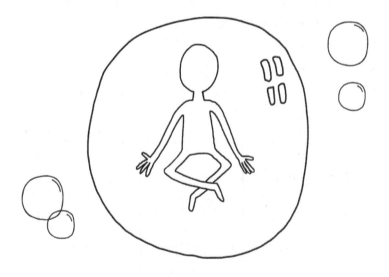

With triangle or slow deep breathing going, spend five
minutes imagining the little bubbles coming in and out
towards you but not being able to get to you at all
because you are safe and happy in the bubble.

Make your bubble thicker if you need to.

You can pop the little bubbles when
they've lost their power over you.

EVERYONE'S A WINNER

LET'S PLAY LOTTO!

Ask the adults at home what you can do to make life easier for everyone and to do your bit. Make a list of tasks and create lotto cards from this list. Give a copy to all the players in your home. Agree a start date and time and see who can whizz through the tasks and be the winner!

Don't forget to agree in advance what the reward will be for the winner.

MAKE MY BED	PHONE A RELATIVE	SHARE A STORY
SET THE TABLE	TALK12	PAIR UP THE SOCKS
TIDY UP	CLAP FOR CARERS	PUT A DRAWING IN THE WINDOW

T-SHIRT SLOGANS

Got something on your mind?

A cause you really care about or something funny you want to share?

Or perhaps a KEEP CALM! tip or instruction?

Create a slogan for this T-Shirt to let the world know!

With the help of an adult, you could even paint your slogan onto a plain white tee with fabric paint if you have some or use a transfer sheet and ask an adult to iron it on. Otherwise, you can use felt pens and ask an adult to spray your design with hairspray.

UP WITH THIS SORT OF THING

Trace or copy this T-shirt as many times as you want and make up as many KEEP CALM! slogans as you can think of.

MY WORLD, MY LAND

While the world is resting, now is the perfect time to create
your own personal paradise by building an imaginary island.

What kind of a place will it be? What will you call it?

Make a map so you know how to get around and
you can invite visitors if you want to. Make a key
so you can show the landscape and features.

YOU MIGHT WANT TO INCLUDE:

beaches	roads and railways	forests
towns	mountains	farms
villages	rivers	parks
cities	lakes	special buildings

What else will be on your island? What wildlife lives there?

Make a mind movie of you and your loved ones being on your island,
enjoying each other's company and having as many hugs as you all need.

SLEEP CALM

We all need to get a good nights' sleep and
this is just as important now as it ever was.

If you're tired in the daytime, it's harder to KEEP CALM!

HERE ARE SOME THINGS YOU MIGHT
NEED FOR A GOOD NIGHT

Favourite teddy

Warm socks

Listen to a relaxation
CD or bedtime story

A drink

A light snack

Quiet

Night light

A hug

Make your own personal list of what YOU need to sleep tight.

If you've got things on your mind, imagine getting
a visit from some space unicorns who will calm
you down and clear your worries away.

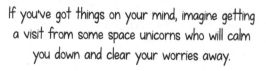

As you lie in bed, why not try one
of the breathing exercises?

Here's a reminder for 3:5 breathing:

Get comfortable. Notice your body breathing in and out.

After a few breaths, start to count along with yourself,
making your in-breath last for the count of three and your
out-breath last for the count of five, breathing smoothly.

DRAW YOURSELF TUCKED
UP ALL COSY AND SLEEPING
CALMLY ALL NIGHT LONG

CERTIFICATE

Have you found helpful ways to look after Bob and KEEP CALM!?

Take a look at your TRY-ARY and see which activities you've used and loved most. Or just have a flick through now to remind yourself. You could add your top three techniques to your certificate, if you like.

When you know you really can KEEP CALM!, award yourself this certificate and put it up somewhere special – your family will feel so proud of you and you should feel proud of yourself. You might feel that Bob deserves his own certificate as well – it's up to you!

Why not award a certificate to your family members, too? They'll be proud of themselves because you recognise they can KEEP CALM! Ask them their favourite techniques if you want to add those to the certificate.

This is to certify that

_ _ _ _ _ _ _ _ _ _ _ _

can KEEP CALM!

1. _ _ _ _ _ _ _ _ _ _ _ _ _ _ _ _ _ _

2. _ _ _ _ _ _ _ _ _ _ _ _ _ _ _ _ _ _

3. _ _ _ _ _ _ _ _ _ _ _ _ _ _ _ _ _ _

SIGNED/DATE: _ _ _ _ _ _ _ _ _ _ _ _

Design your own certificate or copy this design.

THE BIT FOR GROWN UPS

This activity book is perfect for parents and carers, teachers, learning mentors, social workers, coaches, therapists and youth leaders who want to help children stay safe, happy and positive during the pandemic.

Like all of us, children are experiencing the current situation for the first time in their lives. There wasn't a lot of warning and it wasn't really possible to prepare them for the lockdown and social distancing measures, either at home or at school. We are all making it up as we go along and trying to do our best. Aim for good enough and you'll get it right!

During the pandemic, and for a while afterwards, your child may experience confusion, upset and angry feelings, anxiety, or reduced trust and confidence in themselves or others. Children are often very resilient but don't usually have the knowledge or language skills to explain their distress so may struggle to make sense of what is happening.

This activity book will specifically support your child to explore, express and explain their feelings about what is happening right now and open up the conversation with you. The uplifting, calming activities will increase clarity, confidence, peace of mind and resilience and encourage a heathy understanding of their feelings and the situation across the world, enabling them to identify and process their emotions.

TIPS FOR PARENTS, CARERS AND GUARDIANS ON SELF-CARE DURING THE PANDEMIC

The most important thing you can do to help your child (or children) is to be aware of your own emotions and feelings and look after yourself while you look after them. Just as children can't always recognise or express what's happening for them, adults also often struggle with this. The added benefit of this book is that you'll also get the chance to process your own feelings when you chat to your child about the pages they've completed!

You too will learn how to KEEP CALM!

Here's a quick and easy way to stay on top of managing your own emotions and ensure you're well equipped for the next few months of supporting your child.

Take care of your home environment and involve everyone in keeping things tidy.

Activity and creativity are important to your mental wellbeing.

Keep taking any medication you need and order more in good time.

Eat well and drink plenty of water.

Connect with your friends and family often.

Ask for help and access any support or treatment you need or usually have.

Routines will help you to stay mentally healthy.

Entertain yourself with movies, music, books and other things you enjoy.

If you need any help or support, or you just need to talk to someone, you can contact these organisations or speak to your GP or a counsellor.

SANE HELPLINE

SANE's helpline is a national, 7-days-a-week, out-of-hours (6pm-11pm) telephone helpline for anyone coping with mental illness, including concerned relatives or friends.

Tel: 0300 304 7000
www.sane.org.uk

MIND - FOR BETTER MENTAL HEALTH

Provides information on a range of topics including: types of mental health problem, where to get help, medication and alternative treatments and advocacy. They will look for details of help and support in your own area.

Call weekdays 9am-6pm, phone calls from UK landlines are charged at local rates. Charges from mobile telephones vary considerably.

Tel: 0300 123 3393   Text: 86463
www.mind.org.uk

THE SAMARITANS

Listening and support for anyone who needs it.

Contact 24 hours a day, 365 days a year - calls and emails are free and confidential. If you need a response immediately, it's best to call on the phone.

Email: jo@samaritans.org
Tel: 116 113 (24 hours)
www.samaritans.org

TIPS FOR MANAGING YOUR CHILD'S EMOTIONS DURING THE PANDEMIC

It is likely that your child will feel out of sorts for a while until they adjust. You might notice an increase in their negative or anxious thoughts, tummy aches, headaches or tiredness and avoidance of previously enjoyed activities. Children don't have much control over what is happening and will find that hard to cope with. And we adults cannot prevent the uncertainties they'll have to face and that is tricky for us.

Here are some things you can do to help your child KEEP CALM!

- Keep to routines and make a schedule to help you all adapt to this period.

- Eat and drink healthily together.

- Exercise – take a walk, bike ride or scoot together as often as is allowed.

- Prepare to stick to bedtimes – sleep is a great balancer during unusual times.

- Clear arrangements for work, school and home tasks.

- Activities are fun and give you time to relax (see opposite for ideas).

- Listen to your child and ask open questions (see opposite).

- Manage news and conversations about the virus – be honest and keep it simple!

ACTIVITIES

As well as the ideas suggested in this book, lots of organisations are offering online activities – check out art galleries, zoos, museums, theatres and arts venues across the world.

LISTENING TO YOUR CHILD

These questions can be useful in helping you to understand and manage your child's emotions:

- Is there anything you want to talk about?

- Would it be helpful if we make a daily plan together?

- What fun things would you like to do together?

- How are you finding what's happening right now?

- How do you feel about staying at home so much?

- Do you have any worries about the coronavirus?

- How can I help you make it easier to do your schoolwork at home?

- What makes you feel calm?

- Who would you like to keep in touch with and how shall we do that?

- What have you enjoyed about today?

- Where in our home do you enjoy relaxing?

- What can I do to help you with the difficulties you're dealing with right now?

If your child's distress persists or escalates, talk to your GP, a counsellor or one of these professional organisations for support and guidance:

YOUNG MINDS - PARENT HELPLINE

Mon-Fri 9:30am-4pm - free in England, Scotland, Wales and Northern Ireland.

Call to talk through your child's problem. Advisers listen in complete confidentiality, help you to understand your child's behaviour and give you practical advice. They can refer you to a specialist e.g. psychotherapist, psychiatrist, psychologist or mental health nurse within 7 days.

WINSTON'S WISH

Provides support for parents, carers, professionals and anyone who is supporting a child following a bereavement. If a young person you know is finding it hard to cope, the freephone national helpline can offer therapeutic advice.

Online chat: every Monday & Thursday 12-4.30pm, and Wednesday and Friday from 12pm-2.30pm.

Tel: 08088 020 021
Email: ask@winstonswish.org
www.winstonswish.org

ADVICE ON TALKING TO CHILDREN ABOUT ILLNESS

www.bps.org.uk/news-and-policy/advice-talking-children-about-illness

CORONAVIRUS INFORMATION FOR PARENTS OF DISABLED CHILDREN

www.contact.org.uk/advice-and-support/coronavirus-information-for-families-with-disabled-children

THE NATIONAL AUTISTIC SOCIETY CORONAVIRUS RESOURCES FOR AUTISTIC PEOPLE AND FAMILIES

www.autism.org.uk/services/helplines/coronavirus/resources

UNICEF - WHAT YOU NEED TO KNOW ABOUT THE VIRUS TO PROTECT YOU AND YOUR FAMILY

www.unicef.org/coronavirus/covid-19

ALSO AVAILABLE

9781783708994

9781787410879

9781787413238

9781787413245

9781787415898

9781787415904

9781787414624

9781787414631

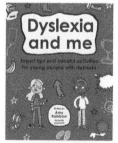

9781787415362

9781787415379